this scissor skill belongs to

- -

BOOKFLOW

Please leave a review because
we would love to hear your feedback,
opinions, and advice to create better products
and services for you!

You are greatly appreciated!

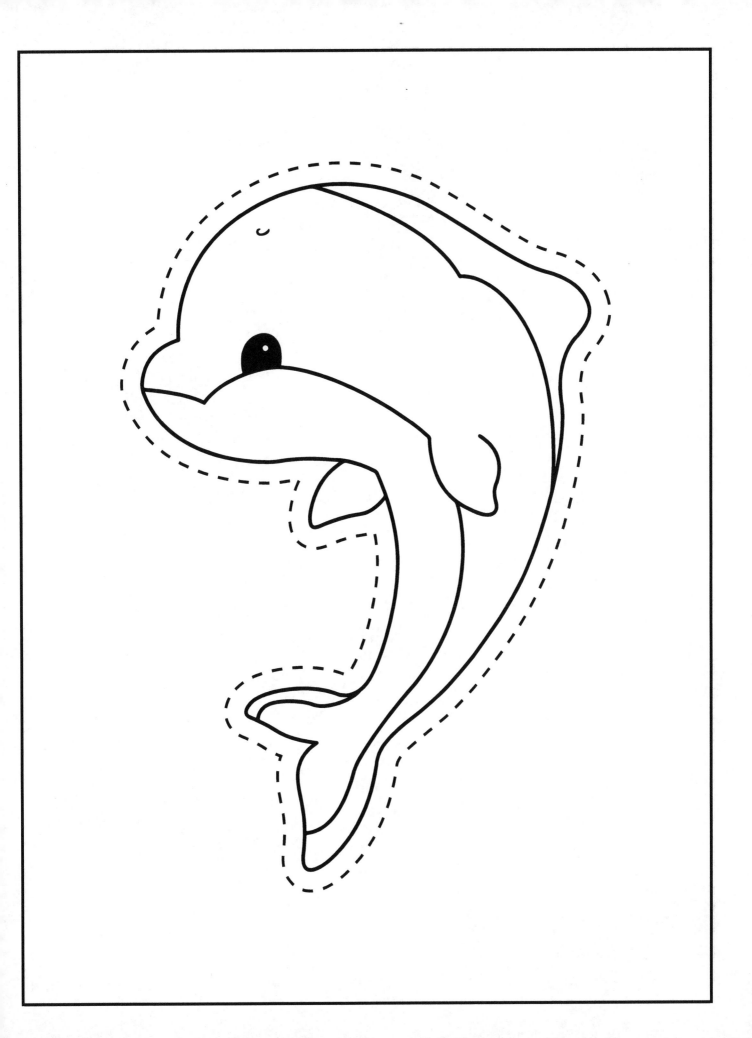

CPSIA information can be obtained
at www.ICGtesting.com
Printed in the USA
LVHW050400110521
687079LV00012B/498

9 785651 765348